CH004154?

Ransom Neutron Stars
Into the Scanner
by Elizabeth Dale
Illustrated by Daniel Strange

Published by Ransom Publishing Ltd.
Unit 7, Brocklands Farm, West Meon, Hampshire GU32 1JN, UK
www.ransom.co.uk

ISBN   978 178591 439 3
First published in 2017

Into the Scanner

Elizabeth Dale

Illustrated by Daniel Strange

Ransom

Jack went
into the airport scanner.

Two Jacks came out.

They had lots of fun
in the crowd.

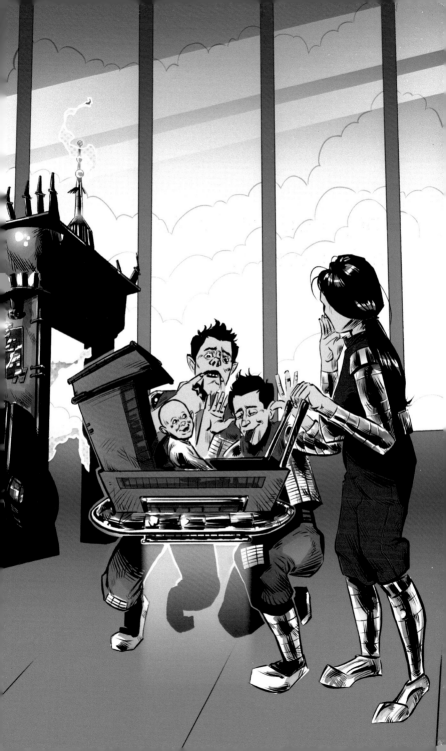

Two Jacks went
into the airport scanner.

Four Jacks came out.

They had lots of fun
in the crowd too.

Four Jacks went
into the airport scanner.

Eight Jacks came out.

They had lots of fun
in the crowd too.

Eight Jacks went
into the airport scanner.

Sixteen Jacks came out.

They had lots of fun
in the crowd too.

Two policemen went
into the airport scanner.

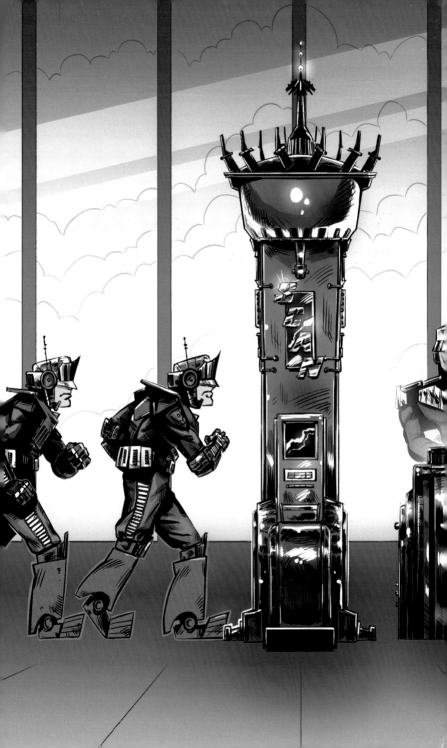

The policemen did not have lots of fun.

The Jacks did not have lots of fun.

No more Jacks!

Good work!

Ransom Neutron Stars

Into the Scanner
Word count **106**

Red Book Band

Phonics

Phonics 1	Not Pop, Not Rock Go to the Laptop Man Gus and the Tin of Ham	*Phonics 2*	Deep in the Dark Woods Night Combat Ben's Jerk Chicken Van
Phonics 3	GBH Steel Pan Traffic Jam Platform 7	*Phonics 4*	The Rock Show Gaps in the Brain New Kinds of Energy

Book bands

Pink	Curry! Free Runners My Toys	*Red*	Shopping with Zombies **Into the Scanner** Planting My Garden
Yellow	Fit for Love The Lottery Ticket In the Stars	*Blue*	Awesome ATAs Wolves The Giant Jigsaw
Green	Fly, May FLY! How to Start Your Own Crazy Cult The Care Home	*Orange*	Text Me The Last Soldier Best Friends